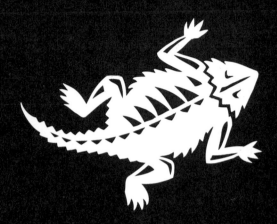

Requests for permission to make copies of any part of the work should be submitted online at info@mascotbooks.com or mailed to Mascot Books, 560 Herndon Parkway #120, Herndon, VA 20170

PRT0712B

Printed in the United States.

ISBN-13: 978-1-937406-18-9
ISBN-10: 1-937406-18-0

www.mascotbooks.com

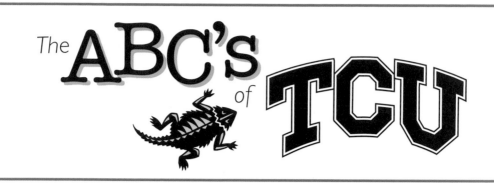

# The ABC's of TCU

An Alphabet Book for **Texas Christian University**

By Sarah Reed | TCU Class of 2010

The ABC's TCU
of

By Sarah Reed | TCU Class of 2010

Welcome, dear reader!
Please come take a look
at my **TCU**
in an **ABC book**.

Wherever life takes you
and whatever you endeavor,
TCU you'll hold dear—
"Mem'ries sweet" forever!

# A

is for **Amon G. Carter Stadium**
where Frogs play football.
It can be a fierce game
but a fun time for all!

# B

is for **bookstore**
Barnes & Noble, in fact.
With textbooks and coffee,
you'll find it gets packed!

C is for **Clark brothers**,
we'll ever revere.
Hats off to our founders,
our thanks are sincere.

**D** is for *Daily Skiff.*
Read TCU's news!
Our very own paper
with stories and views.

E is for **everywhere**.
We're from far and near!
You'll see it yourself
the moment you're here.

F is for **Fort Worth**.
It's where we are found.
From stockyards to art,
there's so much around!

**G** is for **graduate**,
grab your gown and cap!
Go forth in the world,
any place on the map!

# H

is for **horned frog**,
a lizard with spikes.
We're proud of our mascot
that everyone likes!

**I** is for **involved**.
It's what Horned Frogs are.
Just look around campus,
every Frog is a star!

**J** is for **jazz band**.
Come listen, come groove!
TCU's music makes you
dance, sway, and move!

K is for **KTCU**,
our own music station.
It has music and news,
a great combination.

# L

is for **leader**.
Show the world, lead the way!
You'll learn what it means.
Make a difference today!

# M

is for **major**,
a student's main choice.
Explore possibilities
and find your own voice.

N is for **Neeley**.
In business, gold star!
Awards, accolades
recognized near and far.

O is for **orientation**.
Although it's required,
your two days on campus
will leave you inspired!

P is for **purple**,
our lifeblood, our passion!
On TCU's campus,
it's always in fashion!

**Q** is for **quarterback**,
a leader in sport.
There are many others
on field, track, and court.

**R**u is for **Rose Bowl**,
a big celebration
with Frogs center stage
in front of the nation.

Our team was unbeaten,
2010 was a run!
An A-MAZ-ING season.
We did it! We won!

**S** is for **SuperFrog**.
How he loves to cheer!
Catch TCU spirit
whenever he's near!

**T** is for **TCU**,
our lifeblood, our college.
We come here inspired
and leave here with KNOWLEDGE!

**U** is for **Union**.
It's wonderful at night!
The clock tower glows
with a bright purple light!

V is for **volunteer**.
Frogs know how it's done.
Go out, change the world!
It's rewarding and fun!

# W

is for **world**,
what Horned Frogs explore.
We travel the globe
and want to learn more!

X marks our spot.
**Frog Fountain**'s the place.
Meet friends! Take a picture!
Put a smile on your face!

Y is for **yearbook**,
the *Horned Frog*'s its name.
A campus life record
with artistic acclaim.

**Z** is for **zeal**,
**zip**, **zing**, and **zest**.
We know your time here
will just be THE BEST!

So from **A** through **Z**,
you'll see why it's true.
A great school stands here.
We're waiting for you!

# Acknowledgments

I would like to thank three TCU Professors for their advice and guidance through the evolution of this book: Dr. Tommy Thomason of the Schieffer School of Journalism for his inspiration; Mr. Charles Varner for his invaluable illustration tutelage; and Mr. Lewis Glaser, my advisor and mentor for this book and my graphic design coursework. I am indebted to the TCU Student Activities and Leadership Center staff members as well as Tracy Syler Jones, the Vice Chancellor of Marketing and Communication, for helping me discover my passions and connect with other individuals to make this book a reality. Finally, I must thank my family, Dr. Peggy Watson, and Chancellor Boschini for their unending support and encouragement. This book is my legacy for TCU.

# Go Frogs!

Sarah Reed hails from Austin, Texas and was a 2006 graduate of Westlake High School. She graduated from Texas Christian University in May 2010 with a BFA in Graphic Design. She received distinction by graduating Summa Cum Laude with a 4.0 GPA, received Departmental Honors as a graduate of the John V. Roach Honors College, and was also selected as the TCU Senior Scholar in Art and Art History. This book was created as part of her Departmental Honors and Senior Legacy Projects. She was a four-year member of the Chancellor's Leadership Program and TCU Student Government Association and also a member of the Gamma Phi Beta Sorority. She completed the Walt Disney World College Program in December 2010, and a Disney Professional Internship in her field in June 2011, where she is still employed. Sarah is also a US Figure Skating Senior/Gold Test Medalist and skates in Orlando in her spare time.